HELP WITH HOMEWORK
TIMES TABLES

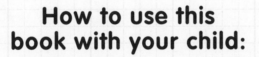
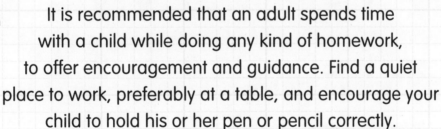

How to use this book with your child:

It is recommended that an adult spends time with a child while doing any kind of homework, to offer encouragement and guidance. Find a quiet place to work, preferably at a table, and encourage your child to hold his or her pen or pencil correctly.

Try to work at your child's pace and avoid spending too long on any one page or activity. Most of all, emphasise the fun element of what you are doing and enjoy this special and exciting time!

Don't forget to add a reward sticker to each page you complete!

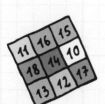

Autumn
Publishing

Complete these multiplication tables.

1 x 1 =		1 x 2 =
2 x 1 =		2 x 2 =
3 x 1 =		3 x 2 =
4 x 1 =		4 x 2 =
5 x 1 =		5 x 2 =
6 x 1 =		6 x 2 =
7 x 1 =		7 x 2 =
8 x 1 =		8 x 2 =
9 x 1 =		9 x 2 =
10 x 1 =		10 x 2 =
11 x 1 =		11 x 2 =
12 x 1 =		12 x 2 =

Reward sticker!

5 and 10 times tables

Complete these multiplication tables.

1 x 5 =		1 x 10 =
2 x 5 =		2 x 10 =
3 x 5 =		3 x 10 =
4 x 5 =		4 x 10 =
5 x 5 =		5 x 10 =
6 x 5 =		6 x 10 =
7 x 5 =		7 x 10 =
8 x 5 =		8 x 10 =
9 x 5 =		9 x 10 =
10 x 5 =		10 x 10 =
11 x 5 =		11 x 10 =
12 x 5 =		12 x 10 =

3 and 6 times tables

Complete these multiplication tables.

1 x 3 =	1 x 6 =
2 x 3 =	2 x 6 =
3 x 3 =	3 x 6 =
4 x 3 =	4 x 6 =
5 x 3 =	5 x 6 =
6 x 3 =	6 x 6 =
7 x 3 =	7 x 6 =
8 x 3 =	8 x 6 =
9 x 3 =	9 x 6 =
10 x 3 =	10 x 6 =
11 x 3 =	11 x 6 =
12 x 3 =	12 x 6 =

Reward sticker!

4 and 8 times tables

Complete these multiplication tables.

1 x 4 =		1 x 8 =	
2 x 4 =		2 x 8 =	
3 x 4 =		3 x 8 =	
4 x 4 =		4 x 8 =	
5 x 4 =		5 x 8 =	
6 x 4 =		6 x 8 =	
7 x 4 =		7 x 8 =	
8 x 4 =		8 x 8 =	
9 x 4 =		9 x 8 =	
10 x 4 =		10 x 8 =	
11 x 4 =		11 x 8 =	
12 x 4 =		12 x 8 =	

Reward sticker!

7 and 9 times tables

Complete these multiplication tables.

1 x 7 =		1 x 9 =
2 x 7 =		2 x 9 =
3 x 7 =		3 x 9 =
4 x 7 =		4 x 9 =
5 x 7 =		5 x 9 =
6 x 7 =		6 x 9 =
7 x 7 =		7 x 9 =
8 x 7 =		8 x 9 =
9 x 7 =		9 x 9 =
10 x 7 =		10 x 9 =
11 x 7 =		11 x 9 =
12 x 7 =		12 x 9 =

11 and 12 times tables

Complete these multiplication tables.

1 x 11 = ☐	1 x 12 = ☐
2 x 11 = ☐	2 x 12 = ☐
3 x 11 = ☐	3 x 12 = ☐
4 x 11 = ☐	4 x 12 = ☐
5 x 11 = ☐	5 x 12 = ☐
6 x 11 = ☐	6 x 12 = ☐
7 x 11 = ☐	7 x 12 = ☐
8 x 11 = ☐	8 x 12 = ☐
9 x 11 = ☐	9 x 12 = ☐
10 x 11 = ☐	10 x 12 = ☐
11 x 11 = ☐	11 x 12 = ☐
12 x 11 = ☐	12 x 12 = ☐

Reward sticker!

Dice problems

Work out the multiplications and write the answers in the boxes.
Use your completed times tables to help you.

= 2 x 3 = ☐

= ☐ x ☐ = ☐

= ☐ x ☐ = ☐

= ☐ x ☐ = ☐

Reward sticker!

8

Creepy-crawly calculations

Write the missing numbers in the boxes to complete the multiplications.

6 x ☐ =

3 x ☐ =

11 x ☐ =

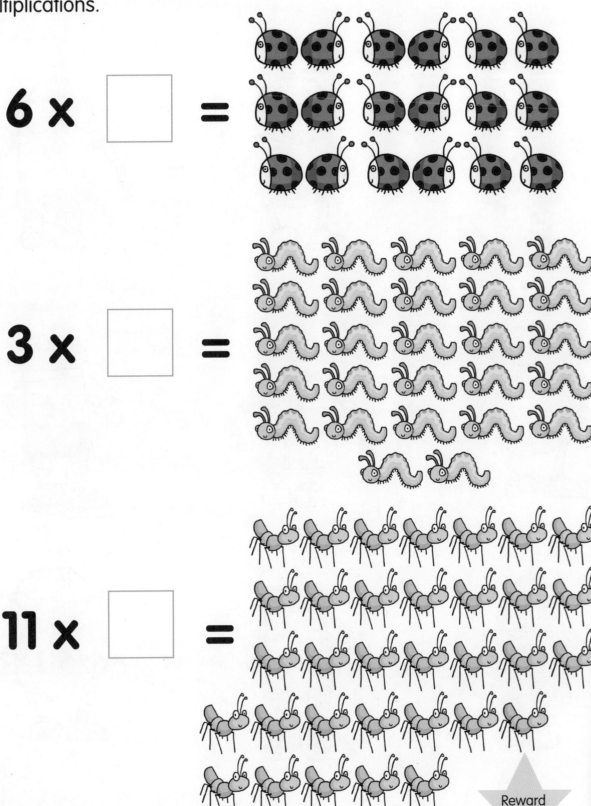

Robot times

Complete these multiplications by writing the missing numbers in the boxes.

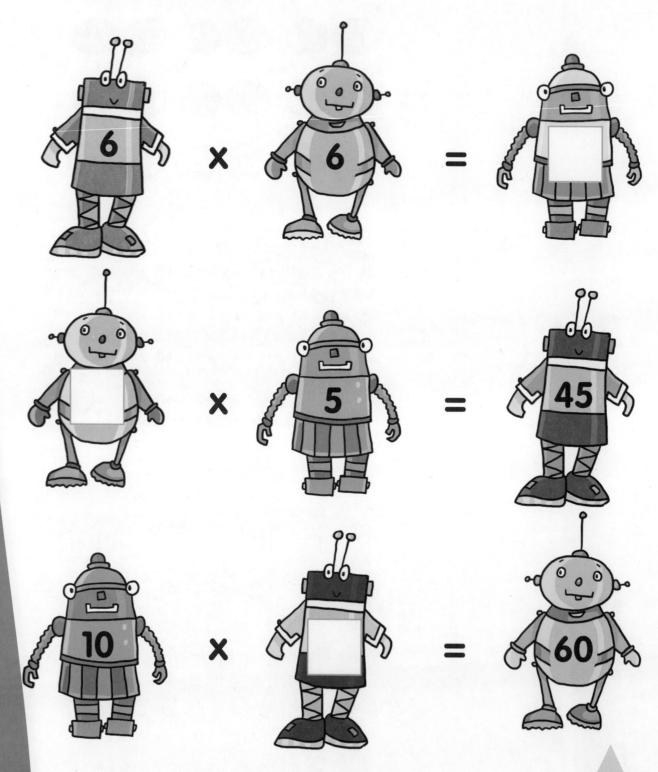

Reward sticker!

Multiplication puzzles

Write the missing numbers to complete the puzzles.

	×	3	=	9
×	■	×	■	×
1	×	2	=	
=	■	=	■	=
3	×		=	18

5	×		=	10
×	■	×	■	×
	×		=	5
=	■	=	■	=
5	×	10	=	

Slithering calculationsss

Work out the multiplications, then write the answers in the gaps below.

10  × 4 = _____

11 × 8 = _____

8 × 8 = _____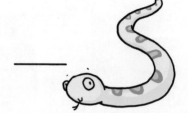

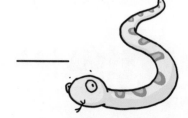

8 × 7 = _____

Galaxy gazing

Do the multiplications, then match each calculation to the correct answer on one of the planets.

7 x 2

14

40

2 x 1

5 x 8

27

2

12 x 4

9 x 3

48

36

6 x 6

15

7 x 5

35

5 x 3

Reward sticker!

Shooting stars

Do the multiplications, then match each calculation to the correct answer shown on the shooting star.

20

0

4

45

16

21

48

9

2 × 2

8 × 0

10 × 2

6 × 8

3 × 7

5 × 9

4 × 4

3 × 3

Reward sticker!

Multiplication puzzles

Write the missing numbers to complete the puzzles below.

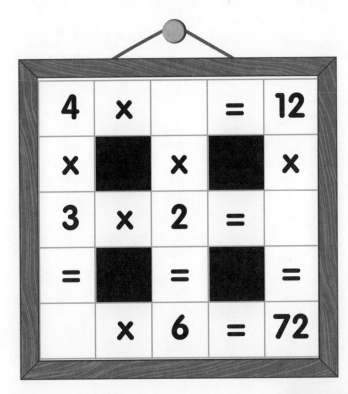

4	x		=	12
x	■	x	■	x
3	x	2	=	
=	■	=	■	=
	x	6	=	72

	x	2	=	12
x	■	x	■	x
1	x		=	3
=	■	=	■	=
	x	6	=	36

Reward sticker!

Number ball fun

Complete the multiplications by writing the missing numbers in the boxes.

(8) (8) (8) (8) (8) = 5 × 8 = ☐

(12) (12) (12) (12) (12) (12) = ☐ × ☐ = ☐

(7) (7) (7) = ☐ × ☐ = ☐

(9) (9) (9) (9) = ☐ × ☐ = ☐

(11) (11) = ☐ × ☐ = ☐

Reward sticker!

16

Painting problems

Work out the answers to the multiplications on the ladders.
Write the answers on the buckets.

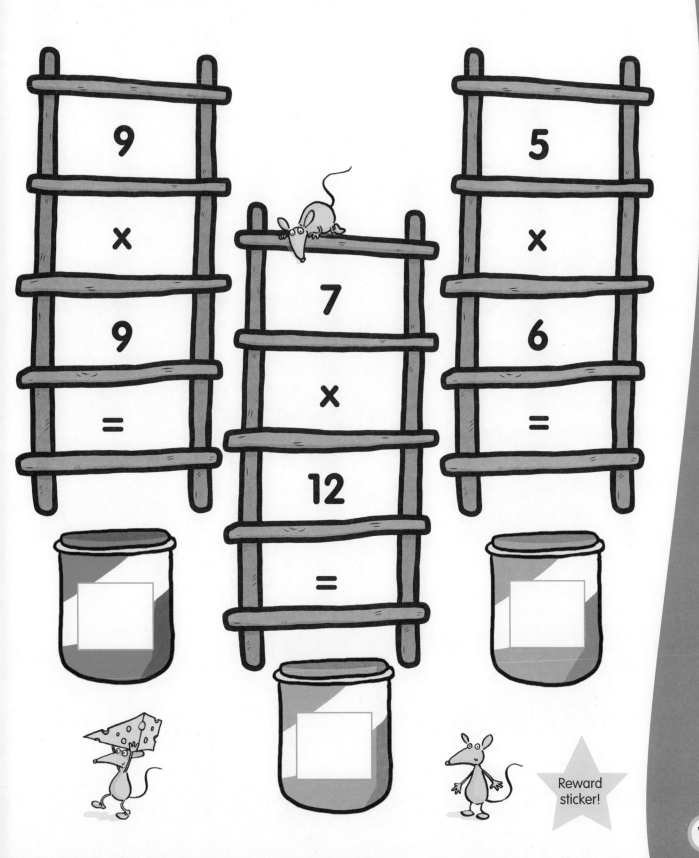

9
×
9
=

7
×
12
=

5
×
6
=

Reward sticker!

Number crossword

Do the multiplications and write the answers in the boxes. Then write the answers as words in the crossword grid.

1. → 8 × 2 = ☐

1. ↓ 17 × 1 = ☐

2. 3 × 3 = ☐

3. → 1 × 2 = ☐

3. ↓ 4 × 3 = ☐

4. 2 × 4 = ☐

5. 11 × 1 = ☐

6. 1 × 1 = ☐

7. 10 × 8 = ☐

8. 9 × 1 = ☐

Reward sticker!

Multiplication stories

Help Wanda Witch solve the puzzling problems below.
Write the answers in the boxes.

If **1** bag of slime makes **3** cups of smelly
potion, how many cups of potion can
Wanda make with **3** bags of slime?

If Wanda makes **3** test tubes of smelly
potion in **1** hour, how many tubes can
she make in **4** hours?

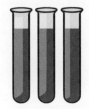

If **5** wizards each buy **5** of Wanda's recipes,
how many recipes will she sell altogether?

Dominoes problems

Count the values on the dominoes, then use them to fill in the missing numbers and complete the multiplications.

× = 9 × 12 = ☐

× = ☐ × ☐ = ☐

× = ☐ × ☐ = ☐

× = ☐ × ☐ = ☐

Reward sticker!

Right or wrong?

Tick the correct answers and cross the incorrect answers.

$6 \times 1 = 6$

$7 \times 6 = 42$

$9 \times 9 = 108$

$2 \times 5 = 10$

$3 \times 7 = 31$

$5 \times 9 = 55$

$6 \times 11 = 66$

$10 \times 10 = 99$

$11 \times 11 = 121$

$9 \times 2 = 18$

$5 \times 0 = 5$

$12 \times 2 = 48$

$12 \times 12 = 4$

$0 \times 9 = 0$

$10 \times 2 = 20$

$3 \times 8 = 24$

Reward sticker!

Number crossword

Do the multiplications and write the answers in the boxes. Then write the answers as words in the crossword grid.

1. **10** × **7** =

2. **9** × **2** =

3. **1** × **13** =

4. **5** × **0** =

5. **1** × **1** =

6. **1** × **2** =

7. **4** × **3** =

8. **11** × **1** =

9. **4** × **2** =

10. **10** × **9** =

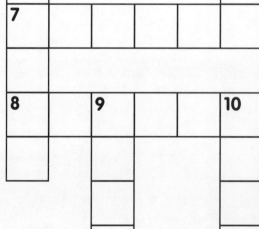

Reward sticker!

Tick or cross?

Tick the correct answers and cross the incorrect answers.

6 x 4 = 24	☐	9 x 6 = 34 ☐
5 x 5 = 35	☐	9 x 9 = 81 ☐
7 x 2 = 14	☐	7 x 7 = 49 ☐
8 x 9 = 64	☐	12 x 10 = 120 ☐
6 x 2 = 12	☐	5 x 8 = 45 ☐
4 x 3 = 12	☐	3 x 3 = 9 ☐
7 x 3 = 21	☐	5 x 10 = 50 ☐
12 x 4 = 28	☐	8 x 3 = 34 ☐
10 x 3 = 3	☐	5 x 11 = 55 ☐

Reward sticker!

Multiplication puzzles

Write the missing numbers to complete the puzzles.

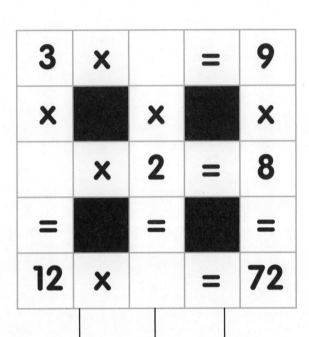

3	×		=	9
×	■	×	■	×
	×	2	=	8
=	■	=	■	=
12	×		=	72

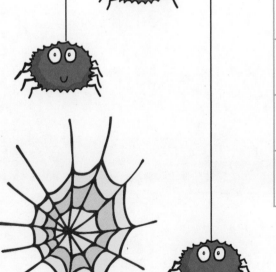

	×	5	=	5
×	■	×	■	×
4	×		=	
=	■	=	■	=
4	×	10	=	40

Reward sticker!

Number crossword

Do the multiplications and write the answers in the boxes.
Then, write the answers as words in the crossword grid.

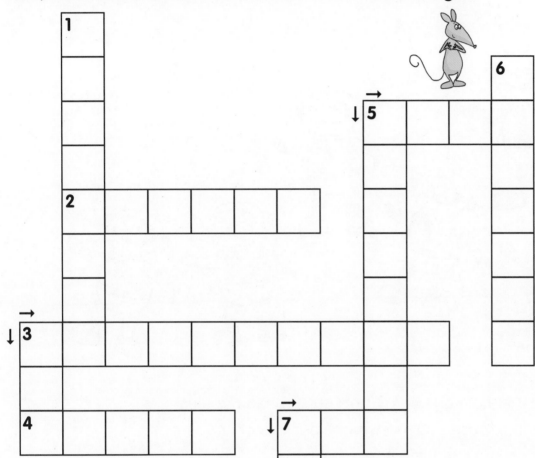

1. 6 × 3 =

2. 6 × 2 =

3.→ 10 × 10 =

3.↓ 1 × 1 =

4. 4 × 2 =

5.→ 1 × 5 =

5.↓ 7 × 2 =

6. 7 × 10 =

7.→ 5 × 2 =

7.↓ 5 × 4 =

Reward sticker!

Problem solving

Help Arthur the astronaut solve these solar problems.
Write the answers in the boxes.

If **6** astronauts can fit in **1** rocket, how many astronauts can fit in **3** rockets?

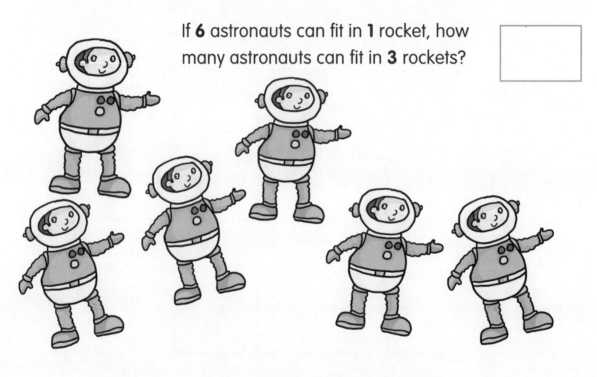

If Arthur can carry **7** packets of dried noodles in **1** space bag, how many packets of noodles can he carry in **5** space bags?

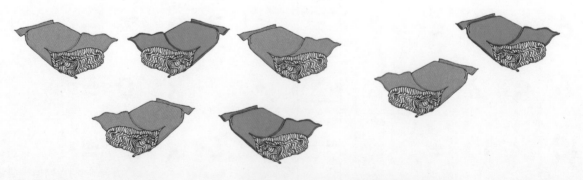

If Arthur can collect **9** moon rocks in **1** minute, how many can he collect in **3** minutes?

Reward sticker!

Jungle Jim

Help Jim swing through the jungle by colouring in three vines.
One vine should use numbers from the 6 times table, another from
the 8 times table and another from the 9 times table.

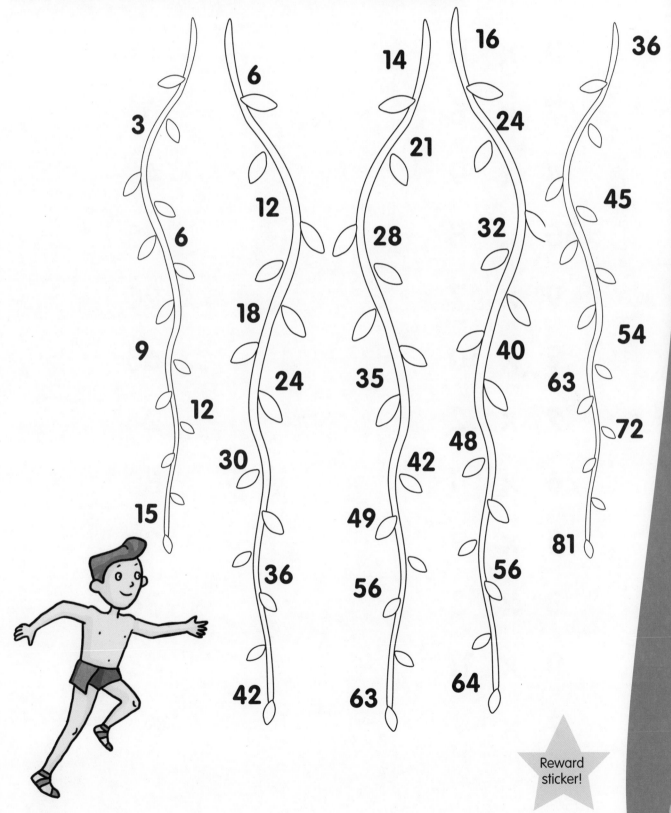

Reward sticker!

Multiplication match

Match the multiplications on the left to the answers on the right. Why not time yourself, and see how quickly you can find all the answers?

3 × 11	144
7 × 6	0
4 × 9	49
10 × 8	42
9 × 7	20
2 × 10	63
12 × 12	24
6 × 1	80
5 × 9	33
8 × 3	36
0 × 11	45
7 × 7	6

Reward sticker!

Test time 1

Do these multiplications. Write the answers in the boxes.

2 x 4 =

5 x 8 =

5 x 7 =

2 x 5 =

6 x 6 =

10 x 5 =

12 x 4 =

6 x 8 =

7 x 0 =

11 x 10 =

8 x 12 =

6 x 9 =

9 x 8 =

1 x 1 =

2 x 2 =

12 x 11 =

1 x 7 =

7 x 2 =

11 x 6 =

8 x 8 =

5 x 9 =

9 x 4 =

9 x 2 =

6 x 3 =

Reward sticker!

Test time 2

Complete these multiplications by writing the answers in the boxes.

3 × 0 = ☐   8 × ☐ = 64

4 × 4 = ☐   10 × 3 = ☐

9 × ☐ = 18   5 × 9 = ☐

☐ × 8 = 24   11 × 9 = ☐

☐ × 7 = 49   9 × 8 = ☐

6 × ☐ = 12   ☐ × 3 = 36

4 × ☐ = 32   6 × 1 = ☐

☐ × 9 = 81   ☐ × 8 = 40

12 × 6 = ☐   2 × ☐ = 14

10 × ☐ = 70   3 × 7 = ☐

☐ × 7 = 77   9 × ☐ = 27

Answers:

Page 2: 1 and 2 times tables

1	x	1	=	**1**		1	x	2	=	**2**
2	x	1	=	**2**		2	x	2	=	**4**
3	x	1	=	**3**		3	x	2	=	**6**
4	x	1	=	**4**		4	x	2	=	**8**
5	x	1	=	**5**		5	x	2	=	**10**
6	x	1	=	**6**		6	x	2	=	**12**
7	x	1	=	**7**		7	x	2	=	**14**
8	x	1	=	**8**		8	x	2	=	**16**
9	x	1	=	**9**		9	x	2	=	**18**
10	x	1	=	**10**		10	x	2	=	**20**
11	x	1	=	**11**		11	x	2	=	**22**
12	x	1	=	**12**		12	x	2	=	**24**

Page 3: 5 and 10 times tables

1	x	5	=	**5**		1	x	10	=	**10**
2	x	5	=	**10**		2	x	10	=	**20**
3	x	5	=	**15**		3	x	10	=	**30**
4	x	5	=	**20**		4	x	10	=	**40**
5	x	5	=	**25**		5	x	10	=	**50**
6	x	5	=	**30**		6	x	10	=	**60**
7	x	5	=	**35**		7	x	10	=	**70**
8	x	5	=	**40**		8	x	10	=	**80**
9	x	5	=	**45**		9	x	10	=	**90**
10	x	5	=	**50**		10	x	10	=	**100**
11	x	5	=	**55**		11	x	10	=	**110**
12	x	5	=	**60**		12	x	10	=	**120**

Page 4: 3 and 6 times tables

1	x	3	=	**3**		1	x	6	=	**6**
2	x	3	=	**6**		2	x	6	=	**12**
3	x	3	=	**9**		3	x	6	=	**18**
4	x	3	=	**12**		4	x	6	=	**24**
5	x	3	=	**15**		5	x	6	=	**30**
6	x	3	=	**18**		6	x	6	=	**36**
7	x	3	=	**21**		7	x	6	=	**42**
8	x	3	=	**24**		8	x	6	=	**48**
9	x	3	=	**27**		9	x	6	=	**54**
10	x	3	=	**30**		10	x	6	=	**60**
11	x	3	=	**33**		11	x	6	=	**66**
12	x	3	=	**36**		12	x	6	=	**72**

Page 5: 4 and 8 times tables

1	x	4	=	**4**		1	x	8	=	**8**
2	x	4	=	**8**		2	x	8	=	**16**
3	x	4	=	**12**		3	x	8	=	**24**
4	x	4	=	**16**		4	x	8	=	**32**
5	x	4	=	**20**		5	x	8	=	**40**
6	x	4	=	**24**		6	x	8	=	**48**
7	x	4	=	**28**		7	x	8	=	**56**
8	x	4	=	**32**		8	x	8	=	**64**
9	x	4	=	**36**		9	x	8	=	**72**
10	x	4	=	**40**		10	x	8	=	**80**
11	x	4	=	**44**		11	x	8	=	**88**
12	x	4	=	**48**		12	x	8	=	**96**

Page 6: 7 and 9 times tables

1	x	7	=	**7**		1	x	9	=	**9**
2	x	7	=	**14**		2	x	9	=	**18**
3	x	7	=	**21**		3	x	9	=	**27**
4	x	7	=	**28**		4	x	9	=	**36**
5	x	7	=	**35**		5	x	9	=	**45**
6	x	7	=	**42**		6	x	9	=	**54**
7	x	7	=	**49**		7	x	9	=	**63**
8	x	7	=	**56**		8	x	9	=	**72**
9	x	7	=	**63**		9	x	9	=	**81**
10	x	7	=	**70**		10	x	9	=	**90**
11	x	7	=	**77**		11	x	9	=	**99**
12	x	7	=	**84**		12	x	9	=	**108**

Page 7: 11 and 12 times tables

1	x	11	=	**11**		1	x	12	=	**12**
2	x	11	=	**22**		2	x	12	=	**24**
3	x	11	=	**33**		3	x	12	=	**36**
4	x	11	=	**44**		4	x	12	=	**48**
5	x	11	=	**55**		5	x	12	=	**60**
6	x	11	=	**66**		6	x	12	=	**72**
7	x	11	=	**77**		7	x	12	=	**84**
8	x	11	=	**88**		8	x	12	=	**96**
9	x	11	=	**99**		9	x	12	=	**108**
10	x	11	=	**110**		10	x	12	=	**120**
11	x	11	=	**121**		11	x	12	=	**132**
12	x	11	=	**132**		12	x	12	=	**144**

Page 8: Dice problems

2 x 3 = 6   3 x 6 = 18
4 x 5 = 20   4 x 4 = 16

Page 9: Creepy-crawly calculations

6 x 3 = 18
3 x 9 = 27
11 x 3 = 33

Page 10: Robot times

6 x 6 = **36**
9 x 5 = 45
10 x **6** = 60

Page 11: Multiplication puzzles

3	x	3	=	9		5	x	2	=	10
x		x		x		x		x		x
1	x	2	=	2		1	x	5	=	5
=		=		=		=		=		=
3	x	6	=	18		5	x	10	=	50

Page 12: Slithering calculationsss

10 x 4 = **40**   11 x 8 = **88**
8 x 8 = **64**   8 x 7 = **56**

Page 13: Galaxy gazing

7 x 2 = 14   9 x 3 = 27
2 x 1 = 2   6 x 6 = 36
5 x 8 = 40   7 x 5 = 35
12 x 4 = 48   5 x 3 = 15

Page 14: Shooting stars

2 x 2 = **4**   3 x 7 = 21
8 x 0 = **0**   4 x 4 = 16
10 x 2 = **20**   3 x 3 = **9**
6 x 8 = 48   5 x 9 = **45**

Answers:

Page 15: Multiplication puzzles

4	x	3	=	12
x		x		x
3	x	2	=	6
=		=		=
12	x	6	=	72

6	x	2	=	12
x		x		x
1	x	3	=	3
=		=		=
6	x	6	=	36

Page 16: Number ball fun

5 x 8 = **40**

6 x 12 = **72**

3 x 7 = **21**

4 x 9 = **36**

2 x 11 = **22**

Page 17: Painting problems

9 x 9 = **81**   7 x 12 = **84**

5 x 6 = **30**

Page 18: Number crossword

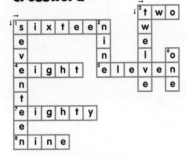

Page 19: Multiplication stories

9 cups of potion

12 test tubes

25 recipes

Page 20: Dominoes problems

9 x 12 = **108**

5 x 11 = **55**

7 x 8 = **56**

6 x 8 = **48**

Page 21: Right or wrong?

6 x 1 = 6 ✔   11 x 11 = 121 ✔

7 x 6 = 42 ✔   9 x 2 = 18 ✔

9 x 9 = 108 ✗ **(81)**   5 x 0 = 5 ✗ **(0)**

2 x 5 = 10 ✔   12 x 2 = 48 ✗ **(24)**

3 x 7 = 31 ✗ **(21)**   12 x 12 = 4 ✗ **(144)**

5 x 9 = 55 ✗ **(45)**   0 x 9 = 0 ✔

6 x 11 = 66 ✔   10 x 2 = 20 ✔

10 x 10 = 99 ✗ **(100)**   3 x 8 = 24 ✔

Page 22: Number crossword

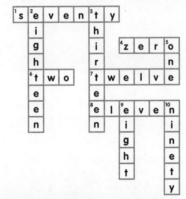

Page 23: Tick or cross?

6 x 4 = 24 ✔   9 x 6 = 34 ✗ **(54)**

5 x 5 = 35 ✗ **(25)**   9 x 9 = 81 ✔

7 x 2 = 14 ✔   7 x 7 = 49 ✔

8 x 9 = 64 ✗ **(72)**   12 x 10 = 120 ✔

6 x 2 = 12 ✔   5 x 8 = 45 ✗ **(40)**

4 x 3 = 12 ✔   3 x 3 = 9 ✔

7 x 3 = 21 ✔   5 x 10 = 50 ✔

12 x 4 = 28 ✗ **(48)**   8 x 3 = 34 ✗ **(24)**

10 x 3 = 3 ✗ **(30)**   5 x 11 = 55 ✔

Page 24: Multiplication puzzles

3	x	3	=	9
x		x		x
4	x	2	=	8
=		=		=
12	x	6	=	72

1	x	5	=	5
x		x		x
4	x	2	=	8
=		=		=
4	x	10	=	40

Page 25: Number crossword

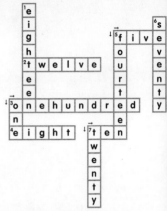

Page 26: Problem solving

18 astronauts   **35** packets   **27** rock

Page 27: Jungle Jim

6 12 18 24 30 36 42

16 24 32 40 48 56 64

36 45 54 63 72 81

Page 28: Multiplication matc

3 x 11 = **33**   12 x 12 = **144**

7 x 6 = **42**   6 x 1 = **6**

4 x 9 = **36**   5 x 9 = **45**

10 x 8 = **80**   8 x 3 = **24**

9 x 7 = **63**   0 x 11 = **0**

2 x 10 = **20**   7 x 7 = **49**

Page 29: Test time 1

2 x 4 = **8**   5 x 8 = **40**

5 x 7 = **35**   2 x 5 = **10**

6 x 6 = **36**   10 x 5 = **50**

12 x 4 = **48**   6 x 8 = **48**

7 x 0 = **0**   11 x 10 = **110**

8 x 12 = **96**   6 x 9 = **54**

9 x 8 = **72**   1 x 1 = **1**

2 x 2 = **4**   12 x 11 = **132**

1 x 7 = **7**   7 x 2 = **14**

11 x 6 = **66**   8 x 8 = **64**

5 x 9 = **45**   9 x 4 = **36**

9 x 2 = **18**   6 x 3 = **18**

Page 30: Test time 2

3 x 0 = **0**   8 x **8** = 64

4 x 4 = **16**   10 x 3 = **30**

9 x **2** = 18   5 x 9 = **45**

3 x 8 = 24   11 x 9 = **99**

7 x 7 = 49   9 x 8 = **72**

6 x **2** = 12   **12** x 3 = 36

4 x **8** = 32   6 x 1 = **6**

9 x 9 = 81   **5** x 8 = 40

12 x 6 = **72**   2 x **7** = 14

10 x **7** = 70   3 x 7 = **21**

11 x 7 = 77   9 x **3** = 27